CW00383004

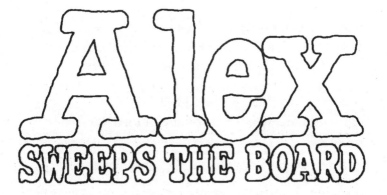

Alex
SWEEPS THE BOARD

CHARLES PEATTIE
AND
RUSSELL TAYLOR

HEADLINE

First published in 1996
by HEADLINE BOOK PUBLISHING

10 9 8 7 6 5 4 3 2 1

ISBN 0 7472 7746 X

Printed and bound in Great Britain by
BPC Books, Aylesbury

HEADLINE BOOK PUBLISHING
A division of Hodder Headline PLC
338 Euston Road
London NW1 3BH

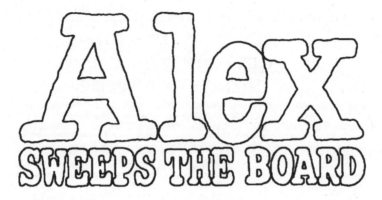

Also by Charles Peattie and Russell Taylor published by Headline
ALEX CALLS THE SHOTS
ALEX PLAYS THE GAME
ALEX KNOWS THE SCORE

CHRISTO'S
"BUILDING
WITH SMOKER"

Alex
PEATTIE + TAYLOR

BUT IS IT REALLY CREATIVE?

OH YES. THE COVERING OF A FAMILIAR OBJECT LIKE THIS IS AN AUDACIOUS GESTURE AIMED AT REDEFINING OUR PERCEPTIONS OF REALITY AND SENSE OF PLACE...

IT'S NOT JUST THE USE OF SIMPLE DRAPED FABRIC WHICH IMPOSES AN ENTIRELY FRESH INTERPRETATION OF SOMETHING WHICH ORDINARILY ONE MIGHT BE SCARCELY AWARE OF...

IT'S THE SUBTLE SUGGESTION OF THE IDENTITY OF A PRESENCE WHICH IS HIDDEN FROM OUR VIEW BUT WHICH REMAINS WITHIN THE PHYSICAL ENTITY OF THE BUILDING ITSELF...

WHEN IN FACT WE KNOW IT'S JUST ALEX'S SPARE JACKET AND HE'S GONE OUT TO LUNCH FOR FIVE HOURS?

YES. WHAT AN ARTIST.

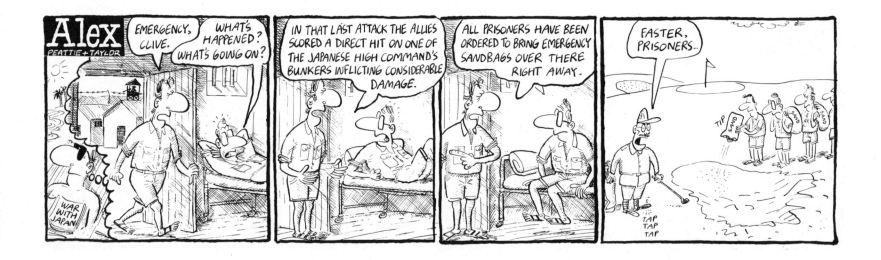

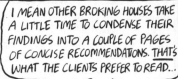

Alex PEATTIE + TAYLOR

So you decided to come in too, Alex?

Well this slack period between Xmas and New Year is when the routine office management gets attended to...

Of course most of our fellow executives don't give a stuff about that...

No indeed. They seem to forget that when someone decides to take time off his colleagues have to cover for him...

Frankly those people who see this as a soft week to absent themselves from the office are in my opinion nothing but slack contemptible skivers...

Exactly.

Any SENSIBLE WELL-ORGANISED SKIVER would be HERE booking himself out for all next year's key days on the newly-arrived planner...

...Thursday and Friday of Lords week... Men's semis at Wimbledon... The glorious 12th...

1996 | FEB | MAR | APRIL | MAY | JUN

Alex PEATTIE + TAYLOR

Of course one of the problems of being a graduate trainee new to the City is not knowing what clothes to wear to work.

Naturally there is a defined corporate uniform which everyone wears, but no-one tells you what it is... You have to rely on instinct to pick it up...

And buying the requisite garb can be expensive... but I'd hate to stick out by not being kitted out in the official expected manner...

SWIPE

ie: Ralph Lauren shirt, chinos and Timberland shoes...

Yes. Otherwise casual dress day would be a nightmare for the uninitiated...

Alex
PEATTIE + TAYLOR

APPARENTLY ALL THE BIG DEPARTMENT STORES THESE DAYS MAKE USE OF THESE SO-CALLED "GHOST SHOPPERS"

OH YES? HOW DOES THAT WORK?

THEY'RE HIRED AS FAKE CUSTOMERS BY THE SHOP IN QUESTION TO GO IN, BUY GOODS ON A GOLD CHARGE CARD, BUT THEN LATER TO GO TO THE HEAD OFFICE, RETURN THE PURCHASES AND FILE A REPORT ON THEIR SHOPPING EXPERIENCE.

REALLY?

YES. NATURALLY THE STORES ALWAYS USE SMART SLOANEY TYPES SO THE STAFF NEVER KNOW WHICH SHOPPERS ARE IMPOSTERS... IT'S A GOOD WAY OF EARNING PIN-MONEY ACTUALLY... YOU SHOULD TELL PENNY ABOUT IT... SHE'D BE PERFECT.

HMM... YES. THANKS FOR LETTING ME KNOW.

FROM NOW ON WE PAY IN CASH, PENNY.

SNIP SNIP

HARRODS CHARGE CARD

HARVEY NICHOLS CARD

Alex
PEATTIE + TAYLOR

NOW KIMBERLEY, ABOUT LAST FRIDAY... I'D TOLD YOU I WOULD BE OVER IN FRANCE FOR A DAY OF CLIENT MEETINGS...

SO NEXT TIME WHEN A SITUATION ARISES WHEN YOU NEED TO CONTACT ME URGENTLY TRY AT LEAST TO USE A LITTLE INITIATIVE AND INTELLIGENCE...

I MEAN, FOR GOODNESS' SAKE WHAT IS THE POINT OF ME LEAVING AN ELABORATE ITINERARY DETAILING EXACTLY WHERE I'D BE AT ALL TIMES OF THE WORKING DAY...?

ER...

SO YOU COULD CLAIM YOUR TRIP TO THE RUGBY IN PARIS ON SATURDAY AS A VALID BUSINESS EXPENSE...?

EXACTLY. SO KINDLY DON'T EMBARRASS ME BY PHONING UP A CLIENT I'M HAVING A NON-EXISTENT MEETING WITH AND ASKING FOR ME...

Alex
PEATTIE + TAYLOR

LOOK BEFORE WE START THIS INTERVIEW:- I REALISE WE'VE MET BEFORE AND YOU'RE AN ACQUAINTANCE OF MY HUSBAND...

ER YES... NICE MAN...

WELL FORGET ABOUT THAT PLEASE... YOU MAY NOTICE THAT ALTHOUGH I'M MARRIED I CONTINUE TO USE MY MAIDEN NAME IN MY PROFESSIONAL LIFE...

ER...OH YES...

THIS IS BECAUSE I WISH TO BE JUDGED AND RESPECTED FOR THE PERSON I AM REGARDLESS OF TAKING ON THE STATUS OF BEING SOMEONE'S WIFE... I MEAN, WHY SHOULD I GO THROUGH MY LIFE ALLOWING MY IDENTITY TO BE DEFINED BY USING THE SAME NAME AS SOME MAN?

ER...ERM...

BECAUSE HE, MY DAD, IS ONE OF YOUR BIGGEST CLIENTS YOU NINCOMPOOP...

OH YES... I THOUGHT I RECOGNISED IT...

CONGRATULATIONS. YOU'VE GOT THE JOB.